· THE JOY OF AVERY SERIES ·

IT'S OKAY TO WONDER

RHONDA WAGNER
ILLUSTRATED BY JIM LUTZ

Rhonda Wagner
Psalm 115:1

LUCIDBOOKS

It's Okay to Wonder

Published by Lucid Books in Houston, TX
www.LucidBooksPublishing.com

ISBN-10: 1-63296-343-4
ISBN-13: 978-1-63296-343-7
eISBN-10: 1-63296-355-8
eISBN-13: 978-1-63296-355-0

Special Sales: Most Lucid Books titles are available in special quantity discounts. Custom imprinting or excerpting can also be done to fit special needs. Contact Lucid Books at Info@LucidBooksPublishing.com.

To
Avery,
my loquacious granddaughter, who brings so much joy.

And, to her parents,
Lisa and JJ,
who obeyed God's call to become foster parents.

And especially,
to
our Heavenly Father,
who can be trusted to write the most beautiful stories for our lives,
"more than all we can ask or imagine" (Ephesians 3:20)!

Read more of this family's story into foster care and their
mission to provide hope and encouragement at
www.messintoamessage.com,
or follow on Instagram
@lisa_messintoamessage.com.

Ever since the Big Talk with Mom and Dad, all Avery could do was wonder.

Swinging high into the sky,
she wondered.

Would she get a brother or a sister?

How old would the child be?

Mom and Dad said Avery would always be
the Big Sister.

Avery wondered and wondered.

During the Big Talk, Mom and Dad said they wanted to become foster parents.

Foster parents are helpers for families who need a hand taking care of their children for a while.

Inside their farmhouse, Avery's parents looked like they could use some help too.

Mom sat at the table between piles of paperwork.

She filled out forms while Dad tacked a fire escape map and emergency contact numbers to the wall.

Mom and Dad would be leaving soon for another foster class.
After today's class, they would be official and then Mom said,
"All we have to do is say yes when we get the call!"

"Avery!" Mom called. "Time to go to Nana and Pop's!"

Avery hopped into the car with Mom and Dad.
She wondered if Nana and Pop would want to play baseball
and fry shrimp like always.

Gazing out at the highway zipping by, Avery exclaimed, "I don't like these big roads, Dad! You know I like little roads best."

"Why don't you close your eyes?" Dad suggested.

"I don't want to close my eyes because I'm very loquacious!" Avery explained. "I love to talk!"

"You even talk in your sleep!" said Dad.

Avery wondered
if that was true.

"What is today's class about?" Dad asked Mom.

"Policies and Procedures," said Mom.

"What are 'Possilies' and 'Proceeders'?" Avery asked.

"Poli-cies and Proce-dures are foster care rules," Mom said.

"Don't we have enough rules?" Avery asked.

"Make the Bed rules, Brush Your Teeth rules,
Listen the First Time rules!"

Mom laughed. "You forgot Get a Bath, Get to Bed rules!"

"Wow, just call us The Rules Family!" Dad teased.

"It's really nothing to worry about," said Mom.

"That's right," Dad said,
"The most important thing for you to remember is that
we need to give our best love!"

Avery sighed.
She was worried.

What new rules would her parents learn?
Dinnertime rules?
Like every Tuesday, they must eat 27 green beans!

Every Wednesday, they must eat meatloaf! And, every Thursday... "We're here!"

Avery rubbed her sleepy eyes open. "See why I don't like big roads!"

Avery jumped out of the car. She ran to Nana and Pop.

"We've got a surprise for you!" said Nana.

"And then, it's time for baseball!" said Pop.

"Yay!" shouted Avery.

She hugged Mom and Dad before they left for class.

Inside, Nana pushed a wooden box across the kitchen table.
Avery wondered what was in the box.

A new book? A jump rope?
Slowly, she opened the lid.

She found colorful beads that sparkled like crystals and shimmered like pearls! Beads of every color! Even rainbow beads!

"Let's make family bracelets, Avery.
Put a bead on a string for everyone at your house, and I will, too!"

Avery picked a sky-blue bead for Dad.
A glittery purple bead for Mom.
A rainbow bead for herself.
And two black, one grey, and one orange for her four cats,
Jaxon, Lola, Tiger, and Pib.

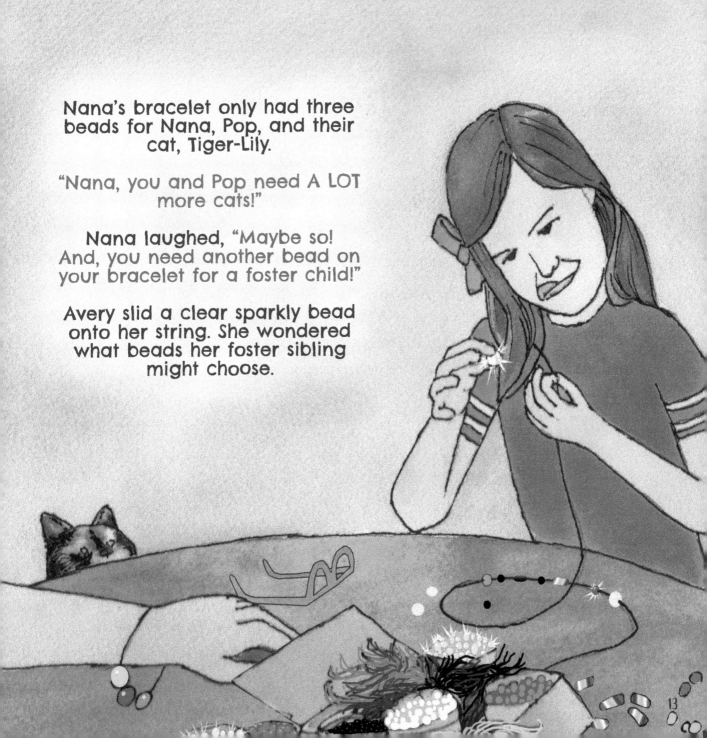

Nana's bracelet only had three beads for Nana, Pop, and their cat, Tiger-Lily.

"Nana, you and Pop need A LOT more cats!"

Nana laughed, "Maybe so! And, you need another bead on your bracelet for a foster child!"

Avery slid a clear sparkly bead onto her string. She wondered what beads her foster sibling might choose.

Then, Pop called,
"Time for some baseball!"

Nana quickly tied Avery's
string around her wrist.

"Great surprise!"
Avery told Nana.

Outside, she hit Pop's first pitch.
"Run!" shouted Nana.

14

As Avery dashed around the bases,
the "foster bead" on her bracelet sparkled.
The sparkles made Avery wonder how fun it
would be with another player on the team!

But a new rule might say baseball
was too dangerous!

Only puzzles allowed!

Uh-oh.
She felt worried again.

After the game, Nana got out flour, eggs, bread crumbs, and shrimp. They peeled the shrimp, floured them, dipped them, and fried them.

Then they prayed,
"Praise the Lord, O my soul, and all there is within me.
Praise His holy name. Amen."
Avery liked this blessing. It was short, and her food didn't get cold.

"Yummy!" she said.
Avery wondered if her new playmate would like shrimp.
Or, they might have a different favorite food to share with her.

After dinner, Avery twirled her beads around and around. She wondered how long the first child would stay at their house. She worried how it would feel when the child left.

Pop asked,
"What should we know
about becoming a foster family, Avery?"

"Well, Mom and Dad said we need to give our best love!"

Nana and Pop smiled. "That's what we'll do. Give our best love!"

"But, there's more," said Avery.

"What else?" Pop asked.

"Foster families have rules! Maybe hundreds of them!
I don't know what they are, but we might have to
eat meatloaf on Wednesdays!"

Nana and Pop looked bewildered.

"Oh, Avery! The rules might be about safety or birth family visits, but not Wednesday's dinner," Nana explained.

"Maybe the new rules are about baseball." Pop grinned. "We might have to run around the bases backwards!"

"That's silly, Pop!" Avery sighed. "I still feel worried."

"Let's talk about those feelings, Avery," said Nana.

"Well, I'm excited to be a sister in our foster family,
but I'm worried about changes with new rules.
So, I feel happy and sad at the same time.

And, what about when our help isn't needed anymore?"

Nana pulled Avery into a hug.

"It's okay to feel two things at the same time.

Excited and worried. Happy and sad.

I'm excited to be grandma in our foster family and worried about saying goodbye someday. But, we can be happy the child gets to go home. Kind of like how you will go home later today. Even if it means a sad goodbye for us."

Avery nodded, "That makes sense."

"We don't have to worry, though," **Nana** went on.
"We can trust God instead. When things don't make any sense,
like new rules and sad goodbyes, He says not to worry.
But, it's okay to wonder."

"That's good because I love to wonder!" **Avery** smiled.

Avery laughed and twirled the sparkly bead.

"Well, I'm not going to worry about it.
But, it's okay to wonder, right Nana?"

"Yes, Avery, it's okay to wonder."

Meet the kitty cats in the story!
Can you find us in the book?

Tiger

Lola

Tiger - Lily

Pib

Jaxon

Dear Reader,

I hope you liked my story so far and will tell your friends about it because more people need to know about foster care! More moms and dads should go to school to become foster parents like mine. There are so many children who need a place to live where families will give their best love. And, the rules really aren't so bad.

If you and your parents are thinking about becom-ing a foster family, please contact a local agency soon. You don't have to worry about it, but it's okay to wonder.

With love and joy,
Avery

Glossary

Bewildered – confused, perplexed (might cause a look of surprise).

Foster care – formal care and protection of children provided by foster parents.

Foster child – a child who is being cared for in the home of foster parents for a while rather than in their own parents' home.

Foster family – a family who has at least one foster child in the home.

Foster parents – people who officially take a child into their family for a while without becoming the child's legal parents.

Foster sibling – a foster child being raised by your parents.

Loquacious – talkative, chatty (someone like Avery).

Policies – plans, guidelines (sometimes pronounced possilies).

Procedures – action steps (also known as proceeders).

Wonder – ponder, think about (a good thing to do instead of worry).

Conversation Starters

Birth Order (page 2)

Foster families have the option to preserve the birth order of their biological* children or to mix the birth order up as foster children come and go within their family. It's an important conversation to have as you become licensed and think through what would be the best dynamic for your family.

- What do you think Avery's parents meant when they told her she would always be the Big Sister?

Preparing the Home (page 4)

There are many things a family must prepare for, think through, and decide upon within their home to meet home study requirements and pass a fire inspection. Some of these requirements may impact biological children within your home. (Example: Will your biological child need to share a room?)

- What do you think about the changes we have made in our home to prepare for a foster child?
- Are you excited that a foster child will be sleeping in the room next to yours?
- Or, how do you feel about sharing your bedroom with a foster child?

Rules (pages 7, 15)

Rules and regulations vary from state to state and county to county, but some rules may impact a family's hobbies or lifestyle routines. (Example: Four-wheeler rides may be prohibited, or permission may be needed to cross state lines for an overnight stay.)

- How do you feel since we won't be able to go on family four-wheeler rides with a foster child? And, we won't be able to spend the night at Nana and Pop's on a whim because they live out of state.

Cultural Differences (page 16)

Oftentimes, foster parents are trained about a child's culture if it is different from their own. Cultural differences can impact the dynamics within a foster family. (Example: The family may serve new foods the foster child is comfortable eating or have to address different hair care needs.)

- Do you think it would be fun to taste a new food you never tried before?

Placement Lengths & Outcomes (page 17)

The primary goal with foster care is typically reunification; however, a case can end with different outcomes. It is essential to talk through the possibilities of placement lengths and the impact different outcomes may have on the members of your family and your family dynamics. (Example: Possible outcomes may be respite vs. long-term placement, reunification, kinship placement, or adoption.)

- What do you think it might feel like when your foster sibling leaves to go back home?
- Or they might leave and go to a relative's house instead. Will you be happy that we were able to help when we were needed?

Birth Family Visits (page 20)

Typically, foster children will visit with their birth parents weekly—sometimes multiple times per week. Talk through how this could impact your family's routines and schedules, how this may impact your foster children, and what this could look like for your family. (Example: Family visits may be weekly occurrences with transportation by a caseworker.)

- What do you think a birth family visit might be like for your foster sibling?
- We might drive the child to the agency for a visit. Would you like to ride along to do that?
- Or, the child might be picked up at our home by an agency worker.

Biological* Children's Feelings (page 21)

It is important to encourage open discussion with biological children about new feelings that are hard to understand. (Example: Family dynamics are changed, routines are disrupted, and departures are hard.)

- Do you ever feel both happy and sad at the same time as Avery did when we talk about a foster child living with our family?
- If so, what do you feel happy about? And, what do you feel sad about?

Roles of Extended Family Members (page 22)

As a family, talk about what being a foster family may look like for grandparents, aunts, uncles, and cousins. (Example: Discuss expectations, preparations, background checks for childcare, etc.) It's great to include extended family members in this conversation.

- Do you think your grandparents are excited and worried to be part of our foster family like Avery's Nana?
- How can we help them if they are feeling this way?

* Biological is used as an all-inclusive word for children who are permanently within a family's home, including biological and adopted children and children under legal guardianship.

Avery is a little girl who loves mysteries and surprises and her little family who lives on a little road. She has a contagious smile with a big double dimple in her right cheek. This very talkative child is excited to live out her very own story to see what happens next. You can find out what happens next, too!

Learn about the first foster child who comes to live at Avery's house in Book 2 of The Joy of Avery series.
Is the child a boy or a girl?
How will Avery do as a big sister?
How long will the child stay?
Right now, it's all a mystery.

Stay connected at www.TheJoyOfAverySeries.com.

About the Author and Illustrator

Rhonda Wagner is a writer who lives with her husband in New Castle, Pennsylvania, where she was born. They have two married daughters and three grandchildren who live in northeastern Ohio. She was inspired to write The Joy of Avery series when her younger daughter and son-in-law became foster parents. Rhonda is passionate about giving her very best love to all her grandchildren, foster and forever.

Find her online at www.RhondaWagnerBook.com.

Jim Lutz is a retired high school art teacher of more than 30 years and a first-time illustrator of children's books. Excited about this new experience, he looks forward to using his God-given talent to touch children's lives in a meaningful way. He lives in his hometown of New Castle, Pennsylvania.

Acknowledgments

Thank you,
Lisa Robertson,
for your valuable insight as a foster parent and your love as a daughter.

Thank you,
Jamie Sandefer,
for your encouragement and knowledge that inspired this first-time author.

Thank you,
Sara Triana Mitchell,
for advocating for the reader with your outstanding edits.

Thank you,
Jim Lutz,
for your masterful illustrations that bring this book to life.

And thank you to my husband,
Dan,
for lovingly giving up much of "our time" during this endeavor.

May all glory be to God in these combined efforts.

CPSIA information can be obtained
at www.ICGtesting.com
Printed in the USA
BVHW090437281020
591967BV00001B/2